Squir

By John Gurnell, Peter

CONTENTS

Illustrations

Introduction

Throughout most of Europe and Asia, there is but a single, native species of "tree" squirrel, the red, brown or common squirrel (*Sciurus vulgaris*). The term "tree" distinguishes it from other types of squirrels such as flying squirrels, ground squirrels, marmots, prairie dogs and chipmunks. The geographic range of the red squirrel is enormous; it is found from the British Isles in the west to north-east China and Japan in the east, and from the Arctic Circle in the north down to the Mediterranean, Caucasus, Ural and Altai mountains in the south.

Many colour varieties are found, the dorsal coat varying from grey and brown to bright red and black. Usually the underside is white and long ear tufts are conspicuous in mid-winter. Two other naturally occurring species have been described from Eurasia: the Persian squirrel (*S. anomalus*) which has a range restricted to Transcaucasia, Turkey, Iraq, Iran, Syria, Lebanon, Israel and Jordan, and the Japanese squirrel (*S. lis*) which is found on the islands of Honshu, Shikoku and Kyushu.

In recent times, tree squirrels from other parts of the world have been introduced into Europe. These include: Pallas's squirrel (*Callosciurus erythraeus*, from Indochina, Bhutan, Taiwan, and the Malayan Peninsular) to Cap d'Antibes in southeast France in the 1970s and more recently to Belgium and the Netherlands; the Thailand tree squirrel (*Callosciurus finlaysonii*, from Myanmar, Thailand, Laos, Cambodia and South Vietnam) to Acqui Terme, Alessandra (1980) and Maratea, Basilicata in Italy, and the grey squirrel (*S. carolinensis*, from North America) to Great Britain, Ireland and northern Italy in the 19th and 20th centuries. The former two species from the Oriental Biogeographic Region of the world have not, as yet, spread very far from their places of introduction, but recently local damage to trees and/or electric wires has been reported. The situation with the North American grey squirrel is very different. This species has expanded considerably from its points of introduction; moreover, everywhere it has spread, the native red squirrel has disappeared. This has occurred extensively in Great Britain and Ireland, but also in northwest Italy. There are now genuine fears that, in time, red squirrels will disappear from large parts of Europe. This concern has stimulated a great deal

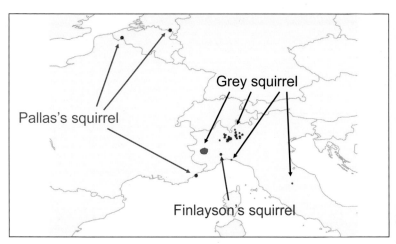

Map: Distribution of grey squirrels and other alien squirrels in Europe.

of research on red and grey squirrels in the last 30 years. In this booklet we describe what we know about the biology of these squirrels with specific reference to Great Britain and Ireland, but also to Italy. We consider what can be done to conserve the red squirrel and what can be done to minimise the impacts of the grey squirrel.

Left: Alien species, Finlayson's squirrel, Callosciurus finlaysonii *- Acqui Terme, Alessandria Province, Piedmont region, Italy. Photo by Sandro Bertolino*

Right: Alien species. Pallas squirrel; Callosciurus erythraeus *- CenterParcs, Meerdal, The Netherlands. Photo by A. Henckel*

Appearance and current distribution of red and grey squirrels

Squirrels, including marmots, ground squirrels, prairie dogs, sousliks, chipmunks and tree squirrels are all assigned to the rodent family Sciuridae. There are some 280 species of squirrel alive today. Red and grey squirrels have a typical rodent pattern of teeth with a single pair of incisors in each jaw, 10 cheek teeth (premolars and molars) in the upper jaw and 8 in the lower. They have an easily recognisable body form with large eyes, small ears, long powerful, 'jumping' hind limbs, smaller forelimbs, and a long bushy tail. A squirrel can be seen leaping through the trees, and jumping across gaps of 3 to 4 metres, or 'sitting up' on either a branch or the ground with its tail over its back, manipulating a piece of food with its dexterous forepaws.

Red squirrels are now extinct in central and southern England, except on the Isle of Wight and two small islands in Poole Harbour. Elsewhere they are confined to a few rather isolated populations in Wales and to the north of England where their range is dwindling; the largest population occurs in Kielder Forest, a large man-made plantation forest that straddles the counties of Cumbria and Northumberland. Scotland still has many red squirrels, but even here their range is contracting, and the same is true in Ireland.

Red squirrel skull and anterior part of skeleton seen from the right. Photo by Stefan Bosch.

Characteristic	Red	Grey
Head and body length (mm)	220	260
Tail length	180	220
Body weight (g)	300	550
Longevity (yr)	6-8	7-9
Autumn weight increase (% body weight)	10	20
Arboreal activity (% time, average for year)	67	14
Preferred habitat	Conifers	Broadleaves
Acorns preferred	No	Yes
Population density (no/ha):		
Conifer woodland	<1.0	<1.0
Decidous woodland	<1.0	Usually 2.0-8.0

Table: Comparison of some characteristics of red and grey squirrels. Dimensions approximate and averaged from several studies.

It has been suggested that at one time there was a race of red squirrels unique to Britain and Ireland, *S. v. leucourus*. This race was characterised by an annual bleaching of the hair during the spring, especially on the tail and ears. Nowadays, these light-tailed squirrels are only seen occasionally especially in Cumbria and parts of northern Scotland. This is probably a result of local squirrels crossbreeding with closely related continental squirrels with darker coats. Several introductions of squirrels from Europe are known to have taken place, especially during the 18th and 19th centuries. Also, squirrels were frequently moved about the country from one place to another. It is likely, therefore, that red squirrels in Britain are now rather mixed genetically. Certainly they vary in colour from pale sandy or grey forms to having dark red, almost black, backs and/or tails. In addition, red squirrels have quite different winter and summer coats. The body coat moults twice a year, in spring and summer. The summer coat is short and often paler in colour than the thicker, more luxuriant winter one. The ear tufts and tail hairs only moult once a year in the autumn. They grow during the autumn and are at their finest in mid-winter. A red squirrel in its full winter coat is a splendid sight. Thereafter the tufts thin out and by the summer may be lost altogether.

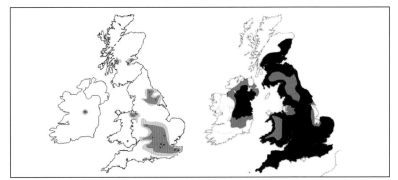

Maps: Range of grey squirrels in Great Britain: left about 1920 (dark shaded) and 1930 (light shaded) (Shorten 1954); right – 2007 (modified after Gurnell et al. (2008a)

Grey squirrels were introduced to several places in Britain and Ireland between 1876 and 1929; they have been spreading ever since, replacing red squirrels as they go. They are larger than red squirrels and only have very small ear tufts. However, the two species are sometimes confused, especially since grey squirrels usually have reddish-brown colouration on their feet and sides, and can be quite reddish on their backs in summer; conversely, some red squirrels may become quite grey in colour, especially in winter. Albino grey squirrels that lack pigment in their hair have been reported occasionally in southeast England, and black or melanic grey squirrels with high levels of the black pigment melanin in their hair may also be found, and especially to the north of London in the English counties of Hertfordshire, Bedfordshire and Cambridgeshire. These squirrels are believed to have originated from melanic grey squirrels introduced into Woburn Park, Bedfordshire from North America at the end of the 19th Century. Within continental Europe, the grey squirrel was introduced into Piedmont (north-western Italy) in 1948, when two pairs from the USA were released at Stupinigi (province of Turin). In 1966, five squirrels from Virginia, USA were released into the park of Villa Groppallo at Genoa Nervi. The Piedmont population spread rapidly after 1980, and by 1999 covered an area of about 900 km². In the early 2000s a population of grey squirrels was found in Ticino Park, Lombardy, Italy, although its origins are not known. Moreover, many releases occurred in Lombardy between 2000 and 2010 (in Italy there is not yet a legal trade ban for this or any other invasive squirrel species), and in 2010 groups or populations of grey squirrels occurred in at least 20 sites in Lombardy. Further translocations of grey squirrels in Italy have recently also occurred in the Venice area and in Umbria. It seems likely that grey squirrels will spread from their current distribution in Italy into France in the next 10-40 years and

Map: Distribution of red squirrels in the British Isles (after Gurnell et al. 2008b)

Switzerland possibly sooner. They could eventually expand over much of central and southern Europe, replacing red squirrels as they go.

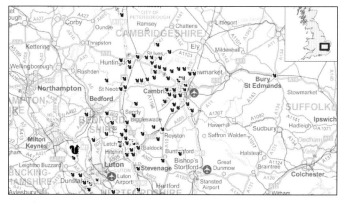

Map: Distribution of melanic grey squirrels in England 2011 (Forestry Commission)

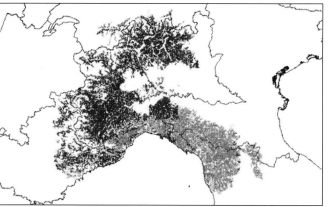

Figure: One example from modelling studies showing the predicted spread of grey squirrels into France and Switzerland by the year 2090 (P. Lurz, unpublished)

Colour variations:

Left: Albino grey squirrel from Essex, England. Photo by John Dobson.

Middle: Grey squirrel in snow, Hampshire, England. Photo by Wendy Finlay.

Right: Melanic grey squirrel from Vancouver, Canada. Similar colour variants are spreading through Hertfordshire, Cambridgeshire and Bedfordshire in England. Photo by Corrie Bruemmer.

Genetics

Red and grey squirrels are not closely related and do not interbreed. Genetic comparisons between the red and the Japanese squirrel (*S. lis*) suggest that they are closely related and in fact may not be distinct species. Apart from this, the closest relative of the red squirrel is the Persian squirrel (*S. anomalus*), whereas the grey is nearest to the western grey squirrel (*S. griseus*) from the Western USA.

Distinct local geographic patterns in the genetic structure of red squirrel populations have been found in Cumbria, Northumberland, and County Durham, most likely as a result of the introductions from Europe. However, some Cumbrian genotypes have been found to be unique and not seen in samples from other European populations. Distinct genotypes have also been described from remnant populations in parts of Wales.

Field signs

The presence of squirrels is readily betrayed by feeding remains. Tree seeds are their principal foods, although they are partial to the fruiting bodies of fungi when available. Characteristic tooth marks made with the upper incisors are often found on fungi. In broadleaf woods, hazel nuts are split open, leaving a small nick in the top and two pieces of shell with clean edges. The shells of acorns or sweet chestnuts and the wings of ash and maple fruits may also be found. In conifer woods, cone 'cores' will be found, sometimes scattered but often in little heaps at prominent feeding points such as a stump or a log. Both red and grey squirrels nibble off the scales to get at the nutritious seeds hidden deep within the cone. It is not easy to detect whether a red or a grey squirrel was responsible for stripping a cone and it is best to confirm the presence of one or other species by direct sightings. There is some evidence that grey squirrels normally gnaw off the scales completely leaving a neat appearance, whereas red squirrels may gnaw off most of the scales but leave untidy strands on the scales giving the cones a dishevelled appearance. However, there is a great deal of individual variation and mice and birds also strip cones. A good field guide is invaluable here (see *Further Reading*). Another sign of squirrels is that terminal tips of branches may be found on the ground, especially in the spring when leaves are just starting to bud, but also at other times of the year. Care should be taken not to confuse these with wind break of shootlets after heavy winds.

Occasionally the tracks of squirrels may be found, either on muddy ground or, more likely, in snow. The hind feet have five toes and the forefeet four (the 'thumb' is rudimentary). All the toes are slender and have sharp claws. Characteristically, the smaller prints of the forefeet are inside and slightly behind the larger prints

Left: Grey squirrel footprints in snow. Photo by John Gurnell.

Middle: The cores of eaten Scots pine cones on a stump, a familiar sign in conifer forests. Photo by John Gurnell.

Right: Cores of Norway spruce cones fed on by red squirrels. Photo by Peter Lurz.

of the hind feet. Squirrels tend to move in a series of hops or bounds and there may be some distance between each group of prints. Although grey squirrels have slightly larger hind feet than red squirrels, it is not easy to distinguish between the tracks of the two species. Claws may leave scratches on tree trunks and branches on regularly used routes. Squirrels sometimes remove bark from trees from the base, stem or crown and, as we will discuss later, this damage is often serious. Droppings are small, round and vary in colour according to what has been eaten. Since they are widely scattered, they are seldom found.

Activity

Squirrels do not hibernate and are active during the day. They start being active around sunrise and usually finish in late afternoon or evening, depending upon the season of the year and how much foraging for food is necessary. Two peaks of activity, one after dawn and one before dusk, are common during the long summer days, but the midday rest period gradually disappears as day length shortens during the autumn, reappearing again in the spring. Not all individuals in a population are necessarily active at the same time. During severe weather conditions (high winds, heavy rain, severe cold), activity may be reduced to an hour or two per day. In extreme conditions squirrels may remain in their dreys for a day or longer. Squirrels, and notably red squirrels more than grey squirrels, store little fat, although this is influenced by habitat type (less fat is stored in conifer habitat) and food availability. They need to feed regularly and lose weight and condition if forced into long periods of inactivity.

Although squirrels are active during the day they are not always easy to detect. They may be high up in the canopy of trees or, if on the ground, they dash to the safety of the trees well before anyone arrives. There they avoid detection by hiding on the opposite side of the tree. In fact, squirrels are often heard before they are seen either scampering through the canopy or feeding on such things as hazelnuts and pine cones. Sometimes the scales of the cone can be seen drifting down from the canopy though the squirrel remains well hidden.

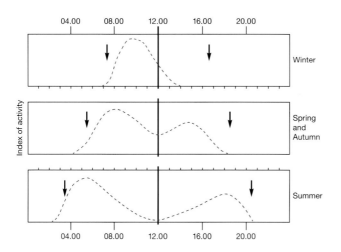

Figure: Activity pattern according to time of day and season.

Nests

The main homes of red squirrels are tree nests or dreys; these are quite easily spotted in autumn in deciduous woodland once you get your eye in. They are round, about 25 to 45 cm in diameter and usually sited near the trunk of a tree or in a fork in the branches. In mature trees these will be at a height of 6 m or more, but they can be lower down in young trees. The outer layers of the drey are made of twigs, sometimes with leaves or needles still attached, and there is no obvious entrance hole. The drey is lined with softer material such as moss, dried leaves, bark or grass. The complete drey is a warm, waterproof hidey-hole. Two other types of nest may also be used. Summer nests are little more than saucer-shaped twig and leaf platforms on which squirrels will rest during hot weather. Whereas dreys will last for several years, summer nests fall apart fairly quickly and need remaking each year. The other type of nest, usually found in broadleaf woodland, occurs in cavities or holes in the trunk or large branches of trees. These are called dens and are lined with nesting material. Squirrels regularly use up to three or

Squirrel drey in an oak tree. Photo by John Gurnell.

four dreys or dens at a time, sometimes more, and there may be many unused dreys in a forest. Unfortunately, there is no apparent difference in a drey or den used by a red or a grey squirrel, unless it has been blown down so that hairs can be collected for identification. If both species are present, they may use the same dreys but not at the same time.

Food

Red squirrels are opportunists and generalists and eat a wide range of different types of food. It is not surprising that trees provide most of the essential foods; the most important are seeds and fruits, followed by tree shoots, buds, flowers, berries, bark and lichens. The underground and above ground fruiting bodies of fungi are also consumed. An interesting observation is that the mycelium of the fungus *Vuilleminia*, which occurs under the bark of dead or dying oak trees, is a favoured winter food of red squirrels on the Isle of Wight. Occasionally insects and other animal food such as the eggs and young of birds are taken.

The amount of food a squirrel requires each day depends on the season of the year and whether it is a young animal, an adult or a breeding adult. Between 70% and 90% of a squirrel's time out of the nest is spent foraging, feeding and storing food. How the squirrel goes about these important activities depends upon food availability and this varies according to the habitat and the time of the year. Seeds, the preferred food, are bulky and contain high amounts of energy. Thus, when seeds are abundant, squirrels find no difficulty in satisfying their daily energy requirements. When seeds are not available, especially in late spring and early summer, many other types of food containing less energy for a given weight are taken, such as buds, flowers and shoots. In consequence, it takes longer for the squirrels to satisfy their needs. When food is very scarce, squirrels may have to spend all their active time foraging but they may still get less energy from their food than they spend on looking for it. Consequently they lose weight. In fact, the energy equation is a little more complicated than this. Some foods (e.g. pine cones on trees) require less foraging time than others (e.g. fungi), and some require more effort to extract the food (e.g. pine cones) than others (e.g. spruce cones). Thus, where possible, squirrels tend to consume as much energy as they can in a given time, but other criteria such as nutrient content (e.g. sodium, calcium, phosphorus and nitrogen) also play a part in food selection.

Conifers provide small seeds, most broadleaves provide large seeds and fruit. In Scots pine (*Pinus sylvestris*) forests, cones are first taken in June or July when they are green and sticky. Squirrels continue to feed on them as they ripen and until the seeds are shed in the following spring. Thus squirrels can remain in the canopy of a pine forest for much of the year without the need to come to the ground. Grey squirrels, however, seem to spend more time on the ground than red squirrels. Norway spruce (*Picea abies*) also shed their seeds in the spring but many exotic tree species, such as Sitka spruce (*Picea sitchensis*) which form the major part of commercial forests planted in recent years, shed their seeds in the autumn and early winter. This can result in individuals relocating in springtime to other parts of the forest that provide alternative foods.

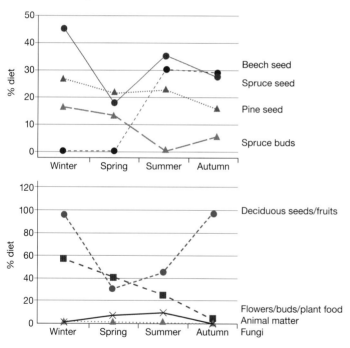

Figure: Diet of red squirrel: percent occurrence of five most frequent foods in conifer forests in Switzerland.

Figure: Diet of grey squirrel: percent occurrence of four most frequent foods in deciduous forests in England.

During the spring, both squirrel species turn to leaf and flower buds, pollen, shoots, and insects, and they may spend some time on the ground, feeding on fallen cones. Energy-rich foods become scarce in conifer forests between spring and the development of the next cone crop in June. Consequently food shortage coincides with the time that most adults are breeding. The same can be said for the early summer in broadleaf woods. Here, seeds and fruits are only available in the canopy between August and early November and squirrels may have to forage for seeds on the ground during the winter months. In mixed oak-hazel woods in England acorns are not favoured by red squirrels and there is some evidence that

they are not able to digest acorns as well as grey squirrels. On the other hand, hazel nuts are highly prized food items for both species.

Irrespective of the type of forest and the time of year, food is patchily distributed. Some trees, for example those on the edge of forests which get more sun light, produce better seed crops than others and they will be exploited first. Generally, as food becomes scarce, squirrels have less choice of where or when to feed. Squirrels usually satisfy their water requirements from their food or from ground surface water such as dew. However, they do drink from woodland streams and ponds, particularly in areas that undergo prolonged dry spells in the summer.

Food caching

Squirrels spend a considerable amount of time storing food during the autumn when food is plentiful. Individual items, such as acorns or beech seeds, are stored in ones and twos just under the surface of the soil and leaf litter; this is known as scatterhoarding. In conifer habitats, cones are also sometimes stored. In one particular study in Belgium red squirrels were seen cutting Scots and Corsican pine cones from the canopy and carrying them down the trees one by one to bury them; a time consuming and energetically expensive thing to do! It can also be dangerous, risking predation by foxes and goshawks. In Arolla pine (*Pinus cembra*) forests in the Alps, red squirrels store single or small groups of up to 5 large-sized, wingless Arolla pine seeds extracted from fresh cones between September and November. These seeds are recovered from their caches the next spring after snow melt; this tree species completely depends on squirrels and nutcrackers for seed dispersal and subsequent seedling development from "forgotten" caches. Occasionally food may be stored in a tree hollow or a drey and fungi are sometimes cut and hung in the cleft of a tree to dry. It is said that squirrels remember the general location where seeds are stored and that they locate individual items by smell. However, there is some recent evidence that squirrels have the ability to learn the precise location of stored food items, but further research is required on this fascinating aspect of a squirrel's behaviour. Of course, it is always likely that squirrels steal the stores of food made by others, as may birds such as jays and other small mammals. Studies in Italy have shown that grey squirrels pilfer the food stored by red squirrels in late winter and spring when they move into an area. The loss of this important food source at this time of the year can reduce the breeding success of red squirrels later in the year. There is no evidence as yet that red squirrels steal food from greys.

Grey squirrels in North America are known to employ another trick: they often nick or excise the embryos of acorns that might germinate early, in the autumn (acorns of the so-called 'white oaks'). This prevents the acorns germinating after they have been cached. Acorns from late, spring-germinating acorns (from the 'red oaks'), are not treated in this way, presumably because they will survive the winter without germinating.

Habitat

Squirrels can live anywhere where there are trees of seed-producing age (from 15 to 25 years of age and older, depending on the species), providing there are enough of them to sustain their energy needs. They live in all types of forest habitats from pure broadleaf, to mixed broadleaf and conifer, to pure conifer but not in all ages of woodland. Conifer forests of between 20 and 40 years of age are particularly favoured because they provide both seed food and plenty of shelter. A mix of trees of different species can also provide a more stable food supply since some species will produce better seed crops in some years than other species.

Grey squirrels come from extensive broadleaf forests in North America and generally prefer these types of habitats, in which they can reach much higher densities than in conifer habitats. Nevertheless, they can live in conifer forest and seem to do well in pine forests. Sitka spruce plantation forests in Northern England and Scotland appear to be one type of habitat in which grey squirrels do less well, but red squirrels can survive in these forests, albeit at very low densities. The presence of broadleaf trees in conifer forests, particularly those that have large seeds such as beech, oak and chestnut, may remove some of the advantage for red squirrels in these habitats. Grey squirrels use these broadleaves as survival habitats and move into the conifer forest when seed cones become available.

Left: Urban park at Legano, Italy, now occupied by grey squirrels. Photo by Ambrogrie Molinari.

Middle: Scots and Corsican pine plantation forest, Thetford, England. Good red and grey squirrel habitat. Photo by John Gurnell.

Right: Sitka spruce and Japanese larch plantation forest, Wauchope, Scotland. Although not good squirrel habitat, red squirrels are able to live in these forests. Photo by Peter Lurz.

Spacing behaviour

For much of the time squirrels are solitary animals. They are not strictly territorial, that is they do not defend an area of forest against other squirrels for their exclusive use (in contrast to North American red or pine squirrels, *Tamiasciurus* spp. in which both sexes are territorial all year round.) However, adult breeding females defend the part of their home range they use most intensively, the core-area, against other breeding females. This is a type of territoriality called intra-sexual territoriality. Squirrels have home ranges that contain all their normal requirements: food, dreys and mates. Calculating average range areas is not very instructive for two reasons. First, core areas (areas where squirrels spend most of their time) are often less than 50% of the total home range size. Second, range size varies with the season of the year, population density and food abundance. Variations in food abundance affect range size in complicated ways. For example, when food is abundant, range sizes may decrease because there is no need to forage for food over large areas, or range sizes may increase as squirrels search out the best food patches. Several studies have revealed that range area varies enormously with habitat (thus forest) type, and even within the same forest there can be a 2 to 5-fold increase in range size when a year of high food availability is followed by a poor seed crop. In fact, if the food supply is poor, then squirrels may be forced to expand their ranges to search further afield, or they may even abandon their home range and disperse to forest areas with different tree species composition and more food. Overall home ranges are between 3 ha and 12 ha in woodlands with relatively high and stable food supplies, but much larger, from about 10-20 ha to more than 50 ha in conifer forests with fluctuating seed crops.

Seasonal variation in range size is often related to mating activity. Breeding males, for example, expand their ranges considerably in search of mates whereas females suckling young may not move more than 100 m to 200 m from the family nest. In general, males tend to have larger ranges than females, except when food resources are poor, and adults have larger ranges than juveniles. The disappearance of squirrels from a local wood where they were regularly seen may therefore be the result of a catastrophe but is more likely to be simply the squirrels readjusting their home ranges in response to local seed crops.

Social organisation

Both red and grey squirrels adopt a social system based on overlapping home ranges. Certain males and females are dominant over others; dominant animals tend to live in the areas with the best food supplies. Studies on red squirrels in Belgium and Italy have shown that dominant males are older and heavier and have larger ranges than subordinate males. Dominant females are more likely to breed than subordinates and their core ranges tend not to overlap. This is more pronounced in conifer than broadleaf habitats. In fact, habitat quality is an important determinant of range size and ranges are smaller in conifer than deciduous habitats. The dominant 'territorial' females tend to remain within the same home range for their entire life. When they move, they do so towards a nearby, vacant area (an area not occupied by another dominant female) of woodland where there is more food than in their original range. Fighting between individuals is not common and the majority of aggressive interactions are between two animals of the same sex. Thus, males are more aggressive against other males than against females, while females readily chase other, especially younger, subordinate females, but will often tolerate a male foraging in the same tree.

Nest sharing, especially in cold weather, has occasionally been reported in both red and grey squirrels. The individuals who share nests may be related, or at least neighbours. Studies in Kansas, USA and in Piedmont, Italy found that grey squirrels form female kin groups. Juvenile males tended to disperse and daughters remained within their natal areas. Amicable behaviour such as grooming, playing and communal nesting were observed among closely related females; aggressive behaviour was directed at non-residents.

From time to time, squirrels make exploratory excursions of several hundred metres away from their home ranges. These usually only last for a few hours but serve to acquaint the animals with food resources and the presence of other animals outside their normal range.

Sometimes an animal will leave its range and not return. These dispersal movements can occur at any time but are more likely in some seasons than others. Squirrels have also been reported to swim across rivers during dispersal movements in Russia. Dispersal away from marginal overwintering habitats to preferred habitats may occur in the spring and juveniles may disperse during the summer or, as is the case with some adults, during the autumn. In woodlands with rich food supplies most dispersers are juveniles and subadults but in forests where food abundance varies substantially between years, or between patches with different tree species, for example the man-made conifer plantations of Northern England and subalpine spruce forests, many adult squirrels disperse when tree seed crops fail. Successful immigration into an area seems to depend on the number of males or females already resident there. Females will settle in an area where there are no other females and where there are sufficient food supplies to rear their offspring; males will settle in an area where the density of other males, potential competitors for food and mates, is low.

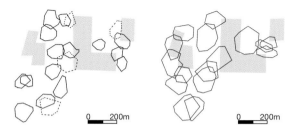

Figure: The distribution of core areas of red squirrels in conifer habitat in Belgium. Left – females: solid lines - dominant, dashed lines - subordinate. Right – males (green area = young stands of unproductive trees)

Reproduction

Breeding activity can persist all year but generally there is an inactive period between August and November. Mating is promiscuous. Male and female squirrel ranges overlap substantially and odour appears to be important in communicating the breeding condition of one sex to the other. Males may leave their marks on branches by urinating on them or by face-wiping, a behaviour that is thought to deposit secretions from special cheek glands. In grey squirrels the presence of a male or his smell is necessary for the female to come into breeding condition and this may also be true for red squirrels. A female comes into 'heat' for only one day and as her time approaches, males begin to pick up her scent and pay her more attention. The males start to follow the female and this invariably leads to a mating chase with three or more males jostling for position at the front of the group. Usually (but not always) it is a dominant male that takes up this position and successfully mates with the female, often defending her against his adversaries. However, other competing males may succeed in copulation; this often occurs after the female has already copulated with the dominant male, who then seems to loose interest (or is maybe simply exhausted) and abandons the scene. Young males below three years of age may simply wait for an opportunity to mate with a female and are called 'satellite males'. Females sometimes break away from the dominant males during the mating chase, giving the young males an opportunity to mate. Thirty per cent of all matings in one study involved such satellite males. Consequently, there might be 'sperm-competition' among the males; genetic fingerprinting confirms that siblings of the same litter can have different fathers.

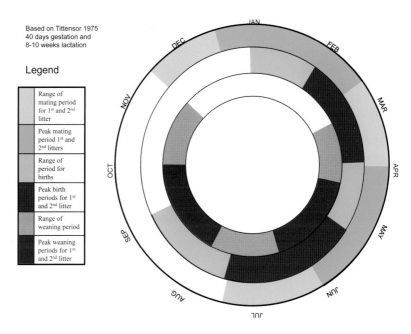

Figure: Annual breeding cycle – variation between years can be expected

Based on Tittensor 1975
40 days gestation and
8-10 weeks lactation

Legend

	Range of mating period for 1st and 2nd litter
	Peak mating period 1st and 2nd litters
	Range of period for births
	Peak birth periods for 1st and 2nd litter
	Range of weaning period
	Peak weaning periods for 1st and 2nd litter

After mating, males take no further part in rearing offspring. Females can have more than one oestrous cycle in a season. There are two main periods when young are born; mating occurs in midwinter leading to the birth of spring-born young, and in the spring for the summer-born young. Gestation takes 6 weeks and lactation about 10 to 12 weeks, after which the young are weaned and become independent. The exact timing of reproduction is greatly influenced by food abundance, weather and the condition or age of the female. Very cold weather may delay the start of breeding activity in the winter and the first breeding period may be delayed or missed altogether when food supplies are poor. Many year-old females skip breeding or only produce one litter in their first breeding season, often because their body mass is not sufficient to sustain the increased energy costs of gestation and lactation. Up to six young may be produced in each litter but more often it is two to three. Heavy losses of young can occur if females are unable to maintain body weight; conditions have to be particularly good for a female to raise two litters in a year.

Squirrels live in areas that are subject to highly unpredictable swings in the production of their favoured tree seeds. Many tree species display a phenomenon known as 'masting' whereby all the trees over large regions produce large crops of seeds in one year, but then produce few or none for a period from two up to ten or more years. Thus, in 'boom' years there may be massive amounts of food available, but in 'bust' years, very little. In fact, this is believed to be an evolutionary strategy of the trees. For example, if the trees effectively starve their seed eaters, resulting in small populations, in "bust" years, in the following 'boom' years, there will be few seed eaters around to take advantage of all that food. In 'boom' years, animal species that eat tree seeds may be unable to breed quickly in response to the abundant seed availability. Thus, there is a time lag before animal numbers build up, so that more seeds escape to germinate in a mast year. However, long-term studies in America and Europe suggest squirrels can beat the trees at their own game. Squirrels appear to be capable of predicting when a big mast crop is about to be produced by the trees and, in anticipation of this, they produce more offspring in the form of an additional litter (e.g. American red squirrels) or more females produce a second, summer litter consisting of a higher number of offspring (e.g. in Eurasian red squirrels). So rather than having to wait for the extra seed to be produced and become available for consumption, the squirrels produce more young well in advance of when the seed is ready to eat but at a time when the youngsters can take full advantage of the upcoming abundant food supply. The cue the squirrels use to 'predict' the future, abundant seed crop is still unknown, but might be an abundance of flower buds or small developing cones in the trees.

Development

The development of young red and grey squirrels is broadly similar. At birth, squirrels are blind, toothless, pink and hairless, weighing between 10g and 15g. Hair starts to appear at 8-10 days and thinly covers the body between 14 and 21 days. The first teeth to erupt, the lower incisors, do so at 20 to 23 days and the eyes open at 28 to 35 days by which time the tail is fully furred. By 45 to 49 days the young squirrels start to take their first solid food and they can climb and explore. The mother suckles the young by way of four pairs of nipples. These become swollen and pink at this time, and bald patches occur around each nipple. After 10 to 12 weeks of life the young have a complete set of teeth (the milk teeth) and they are weaned off their mother's milk. At about 12 weeks they may weigh anything between 160g and 220g; the heavier the young animal is at this time, the better chance it has of surviving its first year. Interestingly, young red squirrels have been shown to grow slightly slower when grey squirrels live in the same woodland. It has also been shown that heavier females produce heavier offspring, although the number of young in the litter may influence this relationship. At four months, the young moult into their adult coat; between four months and eight months the milk teeth are lost, to be replaced by permanent dentition. Incisor teeth are not shed but continue growing.

Population biology

Once weaned, the survival of juvenile squirrels depends to a large extent on the availability of tree seed. On average between 75% and 85% of young may die during their first winter but thereafter survival from one year to the next improves to about 50%. A few individual red squirrels live to 6 or 7 years of age; some grey squirrels may live for slightly longer. Poor nutrition and starvation, perhaps coupled with very cold weather or disease, are probably the most important mortality factors for red and grey squirrels, although many become victims of motor vehicles. This tends to happen during periods of dispersal. A survey of 262 red squirrels in southern Scotland in 2010 illustrates the main causes of mortality identified in red squirrels: road traffic accidents (43.0%), squirrelpox virus – see below (14.3%), trauma (11.0%), starvation (9.8%), pneumonia (7.3%), ectoparasitism (1.6%), and other infections (1.6%). An annual population cycle occurs as a result of recruitment, mortality, immigration and emigration. Numbers tend to increase in late spring and again in late summer and fall during autumn and winter.

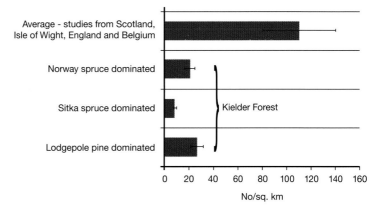

Figure: Example densities of red squirrels. Kielder Forest is in the North of England (P. Lurz unpublished).

In the long term, densities of red squirrels for both broadleaf and pine-dominated or mixed conifer forest average between 40 and 100 animals per square kilometre, but numbers fluctuate considerably on a year to year basis depending on the amount of tree seed available. Average densities in spruce-dominated conifer forests such as Kielder Forest in northern England may fall as low as 20 per square kilometre, and they may be even lower in Sitka spruce forest stands where average densities of 10 per square kilometre have been recorded. Sitka spruce cones are small and contain very small seeds which are shed in the autumn, and thus food is rather scarce in these habitats. Grey squirrels can reach densities of more than 800 per square kilometre in broadleaf forests but have similar or lower densities compared to red squirrels in conifer forests. As well as food supply, weather and disease may play a part in annual fluctuations in densities. When numbers are low, it is possible that red or grey squirrels may become restricted to small areas of favoured patches of habitat. As numbers increase, they spread out to fill more wooded habitats.

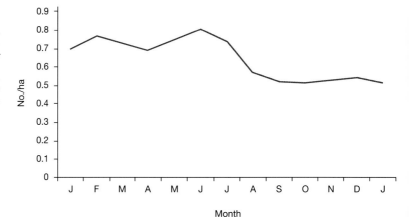

Figure: A typical annual cycle of numbers in red squirrels from mixed broadleaf woodland in North England. Numbers were higher in the first winter than the second because food was more abundant.

Parasites, disease and predators

Squirrels carry a variety of internal and external parasites. Fleas are the most obvious external ones, but lice, ticks and mites are also present on both red and grey squirrels. Infestations of mites can be associated with extensive hair loss. Grey squirrels brought their own flea, *Orchopeas howardi*, with them. There are two flea species found on native red squirrels, *Monopsyllus sciurorum* and *Taropsylla octodecimdentata*; occasionally they may be found on grey squirrels. Ringworm fungal infections have been reported. The gut parasitic protozoans, *Hepatozoon* and *Eimeria*, have been found in both red and grey squirrels. *Eimeria sciurorum* is common in red squirrels and can cause the debilitating and often fatal disease called coccidiosis, especially in undernourished or stressed animals.

Bacterial infections are not common but pasteurellosis has been found in red squirrels and *Bartonella* species have been isolated in grey squirrels from Georgia. Fleas or ticks are thought to be possible vectors for the bacterium. Spirochaetes are known to have been transmitted to red squirrels from ticks in Switzerland. Leptospirochaete bacteria (e.g Weil's disease) have been found in grey squirrels in Connecticut, USA.

Several different viruses have been detected in red squirrels, including one formerly called parapoxvirus but now known as squirrelpox virus (SQPV). SQPV seems to have been brought into Britain from North America with some of the introduced grey squirrels over 100 years ago, but grey squirrels show no outward signs of being affected by the virus. In contrast, SQPV causes a disease in red squirrels that is invariably fatal. Around 60 per cent of greys in England show signs of exposure to the virus although this varies from population to population. Signs of SQPV disease in red squirrels outwardly resemble those of myxomatosis in rabbits. The infected animals develop sores and ulcers with secondary infections on their face, feet and thighs and they usually die within two weeks. Other identified viruses in red squirrels include adenovirus and rotavirus. Both viruses can cause diarrhoea and adenovirus has been known to cause mortality in red squirrels.

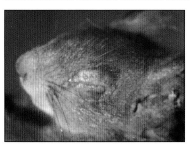 

Left: Red squirrel with exudative erthymic dermatitis and crust formation on the eyes caused by squirrelpox virus infection. Photo by Martin Cooke

Right: Red squirrel with exudative erthymic dermatis on the toes caused by squirrelpox virus infection. Photo by Terry Dennett.

Predators such as pine martens, polecats, wild cats, some owls and goshawks take squirrels from time to time. It is not generally believed that predation significantly affects population numbers in large contiguous forests but good data for a range of habitats and different predators are lacking. Stoats may take nestlings, and dogs, cats and foxes will take a squirrel on the ground if they can catch it. Locally road mortality can be high and rope bridges for red squirrels have been erected on Jersey in the Channel Islands and various parts of the British Isles.

Why do grey squirrels replace red squirrels?

If grey squirrels had never been introduced into the British Isles and North-west Italy, red squirrels would still be found throughout suitable woodland in these countries. As we have seen, there are some differences between the two species in their body weight, build, activity patterns and population densities but these in themselves are not responsible for the decline of red squirrels. There is also no evidence that grey squirrels aggressively chase out red squirrels or interfere with their mating behaviour; hybrids between the two species do not occur. The lighter body weight and build of red squirrels may make them more manoeuvrable than grey squirrels in the canopy of some habitats, such as spruce forests. This may give them some advantage when, for example, foraging for cones on the ends of slim branches.

There is evidence that SQPV has had a devastating impact on red squirrel populations. Red squirrels disappear some 20 times faster when the virus is present in the invading grey squirrels. However, there is no evidence so far that the virus is present in grey squirrels introduced in Italy. So, although disease is an important factor in the speed of decline in Britain, we have to look for other mechanisms by which red squirrels are replaced in the absence of disease. Recent studies, both in Italy and Britain, have shown that the presence of grey squirrels subdues the growth of juvenile and subadult red squirrels, and results in fewer female red squirrels producing litters in the summer. Reduced summer breeding probably results from a lower body size in females, perhaps because of grey squirrels stealing food stores in the spring. However, the most crucial effects appear to be that recruitment of young red squirrels and their subsequent survival are lower when grey squirrels are present. Consequently, adult red squirrels that die as a result of natural causes are not replaced so, over time, the size of the red squirrel population declines and it eventually dies out.

Tree damage and other environmental impacts

Both red and grey squirrels damage trees by stripping away the outer bark, which is discarded, and eating the soft inner bark. Dead bark may also be removed during the winter to line the dreys and dens of squirrels, but this does not affect the tree. Red squirrel tree damage does not occur on the same scale as grey squirrel damage and is only noticeable when densities are unusually high (more than two squirrels per hectare). This has been seen occasionally, for example, in England at the beginning of the 20th century, and at other times in northern England and Scotland. Grey squirrel damage, on the other hand, can be severe, affecting private and public forestry irrespective of whether the trees have been planted for landscape, conservation or recreation reasons. Interestingly, grey squirrel damage to trees within their native habitats in North America is rare. Many species of tree in the UK are attacked, but some, such as beech, sycamore and Scots pine, are more vulnerable than others. The time of the year is important, as is the age of the tree, those between 10 and 40 years old being particularly susceptible to damage. The so-called *damage season* starts in May, peaks in June and July, and may continue into September. At this time of the year, the bark can be stripped more easily. Damage can occur on the lower stem, upper stem or in the canopy.

Why squirrels do this is uncertain. They do obtain some nourishment from the sweet sap, though this does not appear to be the sole reason. It is improbable that damage occurs as a result of a gnawing reflex to wear down their ever-growing front teeth (or all rodents would do it), or that the marks act as some sort of territorial marking post (squirrels are not territorial). The numbers of red or grey squirrels present in the population, and especially the number of young animals, does seem to influence the severity of damage. Aggressive behaviour appears to play a part, and squirrels have been seen to run to trees and strip bark after interacting with other squirrels, possibly in some sort of redirected behaviour. When winters are mild and breeding is successful early in the year, as a result of abundant tree seed crops, the numbers of squirrels present during the damage season will be high and so are levels of damage. Conversely, if seed crops fail, numbers are low, and damage is minimal. Knowledge of tree seed availability in the winter can therefore give an indication of likely damage levels the following spring and summer. If severe damage is predicted, it indicates that more effort is needed to reduce grey squirrel numbers.

In northern Italy, bark stripping damage to poplar plantations can be severe, especially in plantations near parks with old nut-bearing trees or those surrounded by some oaks and/or walnuts. In large park woodlands owners have also reported damage to hornbeam, a typical species of mature plain forests, in particular on young trees (eating all or most of the leave buds) planted to promote regeneration of the woodland. Farmers in the Piedmont area with established grey squirrel populations have also reported squirrels digging up maize. In the near future, hazel plantations for commercial nut production and vineyards are likely to become 'victims' of the expanding grey squirrel population.

Grey squirrels may have other impacts on biodiversity and the environment; they have been accused of inhibiting natural regeneration of trees, serious predation of bird eggs and chicks and out-competing dormice for food (e.g. hazelnuts), but further scientific evidence is required on all of these. However, they can certainly be a nuisance to horticulturalists and gardeners by damaging or eating plants (which can be serious on a local scale) and they can damage telephone wires, electricity cables and invade lofts in the roofs of houses.

High damage - most often reported	
Beech	*Fagus sylvatica*
Sycamore	*Acer pseudoplatanus*
Scots pine	*Pinus sylvestris*
Lodgepole pine	*Pinus contorta*

Moderate damage	
Oaks	*Quercus* (most species)
Maples	*Acer*
Sweet chestnut	*Castanea sativa*
Larches	*Larix*
Western hemlock	*Tsuga heterophylla*
Norway spruce	*Picea abies*
Lawson cypress	*Chamaecyparis lawsoniana*
Sitka spruce	*Picea sitchensis*

Low damage least often reported	
Poplars	*Populus*
Hornbeam	*Carpinus betulus*
Limes	*Tilia*
Horse chestnut	*Aesculus*
Hazel	*Corylus avellana*
Wild cherry/ gean	*Prunus avium*
Willows	*Salix*
False acacia	*Robinia pseudoacacia*
Tulip tree	*Liriodendron tulipifera*
Turkey oak	*Quercus cerris*
Southern beeches	*Northofagus*
Elms	*Ulmus*
Western red cedar	*Thuja plicata*
Firs	*Abies*
Redwoods	*Sequoia*
Maritime pine	*Pinus maritima*

Table: Tree species damage by grey squirrels in Britain

Red squirrel conservation

Undoubtedly, the biggest threat facing red squirrels in the UK, and in northern Italy, is the introduced grey squirrel. Red squirrels are unlikely to return to broadleaf forests naturally once grey squirrels have moved in and replaced them. Woodland loss and fragmentation can also be problematic for this normally arboreal species. The felling of woods and hedgerows for agriculture and urban development, as well as the building of roads, can separate what were previously suitable groups of interlinked woods. Small (e.g. <3 ha), isolated woods that are 5 km or more from a resident population of squirrels are unlikely to have squirrels present. Connecting patches of suitable habitat with wooded hedgerows or tree corridors is a two-edged sword as far as red squirrel conservation is concerned. Such corridors may be necessary to maintain the links between small red squirrel populations in fragmented landscapes, but they can also allow invading grey squirrels to move quickly into red squirrel strongholds. Even so, grey squirrels have been known to move quite long distances through open landscapes so few woods are safe from invasion. It is believed that the only real way to ensure the continued presence of red squirrels in an area is to keep grey squirrels out, if possible, or at least keep them at very low numbers. Extensive cage-trapping on Anglesey has rescued a near-extinct red squirrel population, allowing it to spread; red squirrels were marked and released, but grey squirrels were killed.

In Britain, a lot of thought has been put into red squirrel conservation. It is recognised that any conservation plan needs to be incorporated into management objectives for a designated area which is likely to include one or more forests together with the surrounding landscape. In the longer-term, red squirrels may be conserved by altering the tree species composition and age structure of the woodland to suit red but not grey squirrels. For example, single-species commercial conifer forests can be improved by introducing a mixture of conifer species to include pines, larches, spruces and firs. A mix of forest blocks of different ages provides a range of cover-types and food availability. Also, it may be beneficial to remove or reduce the number of large-seeded broadleaves in an area, especially oak and beech which are favoured by grey squirrels, and new plantings should focus on small-seeded native tree species. It may also be necessary to control grey squirrels in buffer zones to prevent them colonising the reserve. In 2007, 16 red squirrel reserves were identified in the north of England; other regions in Great Britain have done likewise. In addition, research on the epidemiology and transmission of the deadly squirrelpox virus in red and grey squirrels and the feasability of vaccination are priorities (not just "a vaccine", but also how to effectively deliver it!). In contrast, in Italy actions are just starting (2011; see the EC-SQUARE webpage), after repeated solicitations by the European Community to eradicate grey squirrels.

In order to conserve and manage squirrel populations, information about distribution, habitat use, population numbers and trends in population numbers is crucially important. Several indirect methods that do not require handling animals are available. However, most methods cannot distinguish between red and grey squirrels and none are particularly good at giving reliable information about population density.

Table: Squirrel monitoring

Method	Can it detect presence?	Can it distinguish species?	Is there a risk of virus transmission?	Comments
Single-catch Live trapping	Usually	Yes	Low	Only direct method – requires training and time consuming. Squirrels sometimes (eg in autumn) difficult to catch. Traps must be sterilised and kept clean.
Visual surveys	Yes	Yes	No	Visibility problems in some types of forest habitat and times of the year. Frequently low detection rates.
Hair tube surveys	Yes	Yes	High	Possible red squirrel avoidance of tubes used by grey squirrels. Method not tested in many habitat types.
Drey counts	Not always	No	No	Dreys sometimes difficult to detect. Squirrels may use dens.
Feeding transects	Yes	No	No	Only works (cone counts) in conifer forests.
Whole maize bait	Yes	No	Low	Useful to check for squirrel presence as squirrel bite marks are very characteristic.
Nest boxes	Yes	Yes	High	Health and safety problems of erecting and inspecting boxes. Requires training in handling; time consuming to inspect boxes. Licence required if red squirrels expected to be found.

Small woods (e.g <3 ha) and copses can support viable red squirrel populations but only as long as there are links between them so that immigration and emigration can take place. Even large forests, especially commercial forests, consist of a patchwork of areas of clearfell and stands of trees of different ages. Here corridors of trees 20 m wide should be left to maintain habitat continuity. A network of local populations is sometimes called a metapopulation, and metapopulations should be considered in relation to squirrel genetics and demography. For example, genetically, there are the potential effects of inbreeding on fitness when populations get very small, but animals moving between local populations can offset these. Inbreeding can result in the expression of harmful genetic characteristics that may lead to; for example, higher rates of birth defects, lower birth rates or higher death rates, as well as a general loss of genetic variation. Optimistically, it is possible that red squirrels may be tolerant of these genetic effects; they have a long history of wide fluctuations in population size and harmful genes may already have been lost because populations have frequently gone through periods of very low numbers in the past. Conversely, outbreeding, or introduction of "new blood", can result in loss of local adaptations and racial characteristics (like the bleached tail of *S. v. leucourus*)

Grey squirrel management

In Britain and Ireland, eradication of grey squirrels is not thought feasible because control technologies are not sufficient to tackle such a widespread and well-established species. Here, grey squirrels are controlled for red squirrel conservation (by live trapping) (Warfarin poison is not allowed when red squirrels are present) and for tree damage prevention (by live trapping and shooting, and Warfarin poison, which can only be deployed in approved, ready-to-use Warfarin bait). Note that the timing and scale of these control operations are very different for these two objectives. At present, grey squirrels are not controlled on any large scale in relation to other biodiversity impacts. The use of Warfarin poison, dispensed in special hoppers that prevent access by non-target species, is currently the most cost-effective way to control grey squirrels and there are strict legal guidelines for using this method. Research into increasing the efficiency of current control methods and on new methods of control (e.g. fertility control) may be rewarding in the longer term.

The only method currently permitted for the control of grey squirrels in Italy is live trapping. Attempts to eradicate grey squirrels from a pilot area in Piedmont in 1997 failed because the experiment was stopped by a legal action undertaken by an extreme animal welfare group. It took three years to overturn the legal action in the courts, but by then grey squirrels had spread over large areas making eradication very difficult, and for many years the authorities have been reluctant to take up the challenge once again.

Legal status

The red squirrel is not listed in the IUCN Red Data Book or the EU Habitats Directive but is on Appendix III of the Bern Convention (the Convention on the Conservation of European Wildlife and Natural Habitats) which means the Contracting Parties (member States) must ensure the protection of the fauna so listed.

The red squirrel is fully protected in the UK; it is included under Schedules 5 and 6 of the Wildlife & Countryside Act 1981 (amended by the Countryside & Rights of Way Act 2000 for England and Wales, the Nature Conservation [Scotland] Act 2004 and the Wildlife and Natural Environment [Scotland] Act 2011 in Scotland. In Northern Ireland the relevant legislation is the Wildlife (Northern Ireland) Order 1985 (As Amended) and the Wildlife and Natural Environment Act 2011. There is also legislation that protects red squirrels from any wilful act of cruelty or abuse, namely the Wild Mammals (Protection) Act 1996 in England and Wales, the Nature Conservation (Scotland) Act 2004 in Scotland and the Welfare of Animals Act (NI) 2011 in Northern Ireland.

The red squirrel is listed as one of the British Government's priority species, with its own Species Action Plan. Licences to trap, handle or take red squirrels into captivity must be obtained from government agencies (CCW, SNH, NIEA, NE).

In Ireland, the red squirrel is protected by the Irish Wildlife Act 1976 and the Irish Wildlife (Amendment) Act 2000. They are listed as 'Near threatened' in the 'Ireland Red List No.3: Terrestrial Mammals 2009' (see www.npws.ie).

In Italy, red squirrels are protected under the national hunting law (L.N. 157/1992).

The grey squirrel is included in Schedule 9 of the WCA 1981 and the W(NI) Order 1985. This means that it is illegal to release a grey squirrel into the wild, or allow one to escape, even if it was taken into captivity for welfare reasons.

The Grey Squirrels (Warfarin) Order 1973 permits the poisoning of grey squirrels for protecting trees with the anticoagulant Warfarin only between 15 March and 15 August. The Control of Pesticides Regulations 1986 specifies how, where and when it may be deployed (including bait hoppers to be used). Warfarin can only be deployed in ready-to-use bait. Warfarin cannot be used where red squirrels or pine martens occur. Control operators have to be trained.

Further reading and sources of information

Joint Nature Conservation Committee - www.jncc.gov.uk

Natural England - www.naturalengland.org.uk/

Scottish Natural Heritage - www.snh.org.uk/

Countryside Council for Wales - www.ccw.gov.uk/

Northern Ireland - www.doeni.gov.uk/niea/

The UK Red Squirrel Group - www.forestry.gov.uk/fr/ukrsg

Forestry Commission - www.forestry.gov.uk

Ireland - National Parks and Wildlife Service - www.nopws.ie

EC-SQUARE Project - http://www.rossoscoiattolo.eu/en/homepage

Les écureuils en France - http://ecureuils.mnhn.fr/enquete-nationale/

News, research studies and publications can be found at: Squirrelweb www.squirrelweb.co.uk

Bang, P. & Dahlstrøm, P.(2001) *Animal Tracks and Signs*. Oxford University Press.

Brown, R.J., Lawrence, M.J. & Pope, J. (2004) *Animals Tracks, Trails and Signs*. Bounty Books.

Gumell, J. & Pepper, H. (1993) A critical look at conserving the British red squirrel *Sciurus vulgaris*. *Mammal Review* 23: 125-136.

Gurnell, J. (1987) *The Natural History of Squirrels*. Christopher Helm, London.

Gurnell, J., Lurz, P. W. W., McDonald, R. & Pepper, H. (2009) *Practical techniques for surveying and monitoring squirrels*. pp. 1-12. Edinburgh: Forestry Commission.

Gurnell, J., Kenward, R. E., & Lurz, P. W. W. (2008a). Grey Squirrel *Sciurus carolinensis*. *Mammals of the British Isles: Handbook, 4th edition* (eds S. Harris & D. W. Yalden). The Mammal Society, Southampton.